Shining Brass

Book 2, Grades 4 & 5

Piano Accompaniment B♭

For use with

Trumpet · B♭ Cornet · Flugelhorn · Trombone
Baritone · Euphonium · B♭ Bass · B♭ Tuba

Composers
Tom Davoren, John Frith, Timothy Jackson, Peter Meechan,
Lucy Pankhurst and David A. Stowell

Project consultant
Nicky Daw

ABRSM

First published in 2012 by ABRSM (Publishing) Ltd, a wholly owned subsidiary of ABRSM,
4 London Wall Place, London EC2Y 5AU, United Kingdom

Reprinted in 2012, 2014, 2016, 2017

ISBN 978 1 84849 445 9
AB 3699

A CIP catalogue for this book is available from The British Library.

Cover design by www.adamhaystudio.com
Music origination by Andrew Jones
Printed in England by Caligraving Ltd, Thetford, Norfolk, on materials from sustainable sources

With particular thanks to Alan Bullard for his contribution to this project.

Contents

(Pianists should note that the solo line printed above the accompaniment reproduces the 𝄞 Brass part.)

Beaufort Allegro

Tom Davoren

★ The mordents in the solo part are optional and not required in an ABRSM exam.

22
mf
f
30
mp
38
p legato
45
f robusto

53
mf giocoso
mf giocoso
61
69
mp
mf
mp marcato
mf
77
f
f

Folk Song

Lucy Pankhurst

★ The trills are optional and not required in an ABRSM exam.

12
8va
16
mp
(8)
p
19
loco
mf
f
Ped.

23
p
(tr)
(8)
pp
27
f
ff
sfp
sfp
sfp
p
31
f
(tr)
sim.
f
sim.
8va
p
ff

Jiggedy Jig

John Frith

16
sfp
f
p
sf
21
tr
cresc.
26
cresc.
mf
mf cresc.

31
Tranquillo ♩. = 72
f
mp più legato
f
p legatissimo
con Ped.
36
41
46
poco accel.
p
p cresc.

51
a tempo
mf
f
mf
56
cresc.
tr
fp cresc.
61
mf
(tr)
mf
f marcato
f
66
mp cresc.
mp cresc.
f
f
sf

Bragtime

John Frith

Ragtime (molto moderato) ♩ = 80

16
21
mp cresc.
mp cresc.
f
f
27
p cresc.
p cresc.
32
mf cresc.
mf cresc.
f
f
sf

Open Plains

David A. Stowell

20
24
29
34

Way Down South

Peter Meechan

16
ff
ff
20
mp
mp
24
cresc.
cresc.
27
ff
mp cresc.
ff
ff
mp cresc.
ff

Caber Dance

John Frith

★ Trombonists should ignore grace note indications.

★ The trills are optional and not required in an ABRSM exam.

Canzona

John Frith

13
17
p cresc.
p cresc.
21
f
f p

25
p
29
mf
cresc.
mf
cresc.
rall.
32
f
p
ff
f
p
ff

Jam Bouree

David A. Stowell

★ Notes and ornaments in brackets are optional and not required in an ABRSM exam. The bracketed notes can be treated as optional breath marks.

11
14
17
20
mp staccato
mp staccato

23
26
f
mf staccato
f
mp
29
32
f
mf
mf
f
molto rit.
f

Final Thought

Peter Meechan

10
mp
mf
13
pp
pp
16
mp cresc.
f

19
3
f
3
ff
22
ff
25
28

Gone, Not Forgotten

Lucy Pankhurst

★ Trombonists should ignore grace note indications.

8
mf
p
poco a poco agitato
p
11
Più mosso ♩. = 48
ff
f
f
mf
14
p
mf
f

17
Ancora più mosso ♩. = 54
f
ff
f
ff
f
19
rall.
mp
f
non dim.
non dim.
22
Tempo primo
p
pp
8va
pp

for Lindy Tennent-Brown

Lindy Hop!

Tom Davoren

Up-tempo swing ♩ = 108

17
f
f
21
fp
mf
25
mp
29
f
mf
cresc.
f

33
mf
37
41
ff
gliss.
45
f legato
Ped. ad lib.

49
p legato
p
55
mp
delicatissimo
non Ped.
60
mp
p
65
mp legato
mf
legato
d. ad lib.

71
mp dolce
mf marcato
p delicatissimo
non Ped.
76
mf
mf
81
85

89
mf
93
f legato
3
97
cresc.
cresc.
101
ff
p
ff
p
ff